Tr
Gl

Sound at Sight

singing

Book 3

Grades 6–8

Published by:
Trinity College London
89 Albert Embankment
London SE1 7TP UK

T +44 (0)20 7820 6100
F +44 (0)20 7820 6161
E music@trinityguildhall.co.uk
www.trinityguildhall.co.uk

Printed in England by Halstan & Co. Ltd, Amersham, Bucks.

Sound at sight

Playing or singing music that has not been seen before is a necessary part of any musician's life, and the exploration of a new piece should be an enjoyable and stimulating process.

Reading music requires two main things: first, the ability to grasp the meaning of music notation on the page; second, the ability to convert what is seen into sound and perform the piece. This involves imagining the sound of the music before playing or singing it. This in turn implies familiarity with intervals, rhythmic patterns, textures and dynamics. The material in this series will help singers develop their skills and build confidence.

Plenty of pieces are given throughout, making this a thoroughly practical course in developing sight reading skills, whether it is used for examination preparation or to increase confidence in the context of solo singing or choral work.

Trinity's sight reading requirements are stepped progressively between Initial and Grade 8, with manageable increases in difficulty between each grade. Some tips on examination preparation are given at the back of the book. In all cases, however, references to examination tests are avoided until *after* the relevant material has been practised. This is deliberate: many pupils find the prospect of being tested on sight reading skills to be quite inhibiting at first. The aim is to perform new pieces—the fact that they may be examination tests as well is far less important.

Acknowledgements

Thanks are due to the many composers who have contributed to the series: James Burden, Humphrey Clucas, Colin Cowles, David Dawson, Sébastien Dédis, Peter Fribbins, David Gaukroger, Robin Hagues, Amy Harris, Peter Lawson, Jonathan Paxman, Danielle Perrett and Michael Zev Gordon.

Thanks are also due to Luise Horrocks, Geraint John, Harold Jones, Joanna Leslie, Anne Smillie and Eric Tebbett for their technical advice.

The *udjat* symbol is an Egyptian hieroglyph called the 'sound eye', and was associated with the god Horus.

• Introduction

If you have worked through Books 1 and 2 in this series, you will already be quite experienced in sight reading with an accompaniment.

However, as a singer, you will also have to read music which is unaccompanied, and this poses an extra challenge. An accompaniment can give you confidence, and the harmonic progressions can provide useful hints about where to find the next note. When there is no accompaniment, you are on your own.

It is essential that you start with a good foundation in aural training. Make sure that you are thoroughly at home with pitching intervals both up and down from any note of the scale, major and minor. (Trinity's *Vocal Exercises* Book 1 will help with this.) Singing is not about individual intervals—it is about intervals in context. Get to know what it feels like to sing a sixth from each note within a scale, for example: notice how some are major and some are minor sixths. Then choose one type (either major or minor sixth) and sing absolute intervals from each note of the scale, noticing this time how the notes that are outside the key 'feel' in the voice.

Notes of the tonic chord can help if you are not certain about the sound of any of the intervals. Remember: each note is no more than one step away from a note of the tonic chord. A note may be repeated with other notes in between: think back to the reference note in order to keep on course.

Another thing to look for in melodies at this level is modulation. Try to notice if the modulation is going to a sharper/higher key (dominant, relative major, supertonic etc) or a flatter/lower one (subdominant, relative minor etc). Try to hear the sound of the new tonic in your head each time the music changes key.

Even if you can get around the intervals of an unaccompanied piece, if one interval is slightly too large or too small it can upset the whole melodic line. Here are a few tips that you should bear in mind.

- Rising melodies tend to go flat. Aim for wide semitones, tones and major thirds especially.

- Falling melodies can also go flat. Aim for small semitones and minor thirds especially.

- Repeated notes can easily slip a little. Listen carefully, and 'think up' the repeated notes so that they remain in the centre of the pitch.

- If the melody returns to a note with others in between, listen carefully to make sure that you do return to exactly the same pitch. Once again, 'think up' this pitch especially after lower notes have intervened.

It may be a good idea to sing through again some of the exercises that you have already done from **Sound at Sight** Books 1 and 2, but without the accompaniment this time.

Try the pitching exercises in Trinity *Vocal Exercises* Book 2 (high or low edition). It is worth memorising these and repeating them often. Always practise pitching exercises with full attention.

Most vocal music has words. As in Books 1 and 2, the exercises in this book do not. Although this may seem artificial, it helps you to concentrate on the notes. It is suggested that you sing on [ɑ] or [ɪ] and use a light consonant on repeated notes and the first note of slurred groups. Either [l] or [d] will work well. You can also use sol-fa names or any other vowel sounds, with or without consonants, if you prefer.

Each exercise in this book is presented in high and low treble clef and bass clef transpositions.

• Fluency, rhythmic detail, dynamics and phrasing

In these exercises you will develop even pace and fluency, rhythmic accuracy and effective phrasing. Try to observe the dynamics and as much detail as possible.

1

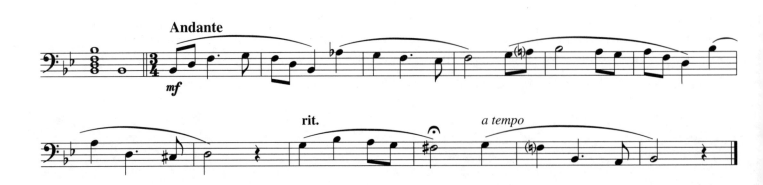

2

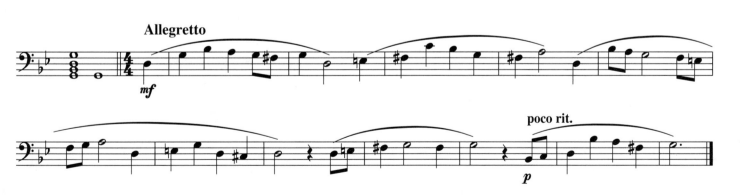

3

4

5

6

7

8

9

 Melodies 1–9 are of the standard used by Trinity for Grade 6 examinations.

• Colour and style

As pieces become longer, there should be increased understanding of the whole shape of the piece and how smaller phrases build to make the larger shape. Recognising and reproducing an appropriate style is important: use different colours depending on the style. Chromaticism will also become more common now.

10

11

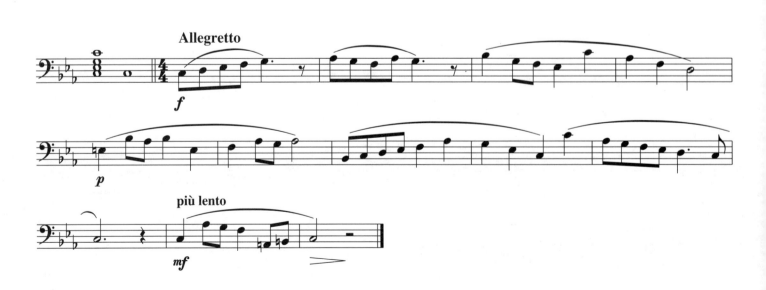

12

13

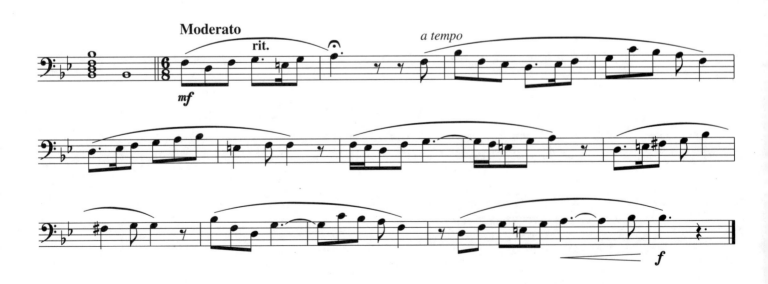

14

15

16

17

18

Melodies 10–18 are of the standard used by Trinity for Grade 7 examinations.

• Increasing variety

You will now be required to sing in an even wider variety of keys and styles. As the melodies become longer, you need to think carefully about phrasing and the overall shape of each piece. There will be more detail to take in, with more variety in articulation and dynamics to include while maintaining the flow of the music. Rhythmic elements become increasingly important in defining the character of pieces.

19

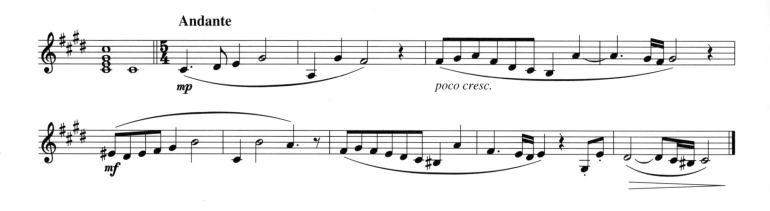

20

21

22

23

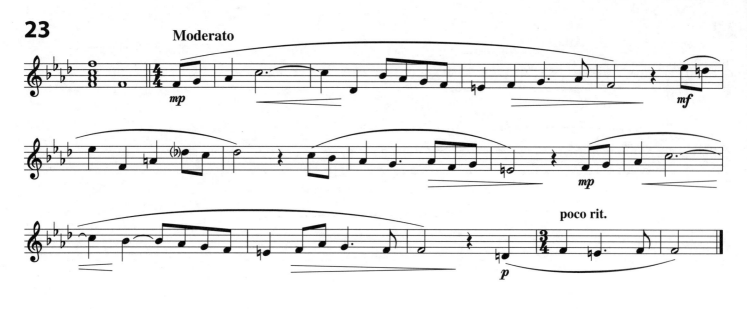

24

25

26

27

 Melodies 19–24 are of the standard used by Trinity for Grade 8 examinations.

• Examination preparation

In an examination, you have half a minute to prepare your performance of the sight reading test. The examiner will play the tonic chord and the key note before you read through the music.

It is important to use this time wisely. First of all, notice the key and time signature. Establish the first note. You might want to remind yourself of where the semitones occur. Look for any accidentals, particularly when they apply to more than one note in the bar. Plan your breathing and any large intervals or changes of key.

Set a pulse securely in your head and read through the test, imagining the sound. It might help to clap or tap the rhythm but the most important thing is to get a clear idea of what the music will sound like. You can also try out any part of the test if you want to, although it is often a good idea not to do this until you have read through the piece first.

Have you imagined the effect of the dynamics?

When the examiner asks you to sing the piece, you will be given the tonic chord and key note again. The rhythm is more important than anything else: keep going at all costs! If you make a little slip, do not try to go back and change it—the moment has already gone. Make sure instead that you concentrate on the next passage.

Give a real performance of the piece. If you can sing the pieces in this book, you will be well prepared for examination sight reading, so enjoy the opportunity to sing music that you did not know before.

How to enter grade examinations

For further information about Trinity College *London*'s grade examinations
please contact your local examination centre representative or

Trinity College *London*
89 Albert Embankment
London
SE1 7TP, UK

Tel +44 (0)20 7820 6100
Fax +44 (0)20 7820 6161
e-mail music@trinitycollege.co.uk

All syllabuses can be downloaded from the website at
www.trinitycollege.co.uk